PRENTICE HALL

# UNITED STATES HISTORY

## All-in-One
## Teaching Resources

---

## The Vietnam War Era
## (1954–1975)

PEARSON

Prentice
Hall

Upper Saddle River, New Jersey
Boston, Massachusetts

CUR
417
PH
9-12
2008
TR
1954-1975

\* Modify this worksheet for differentiated instruction. See other Teaching Resource chapter books for ideas.

## Acknowledgements

**Page 23:** Excerpt from "The Things They Carried" from THE THINGS THEY CARRIED by Tim O'Brien. Copyright © 1990 by Tim O'Brien. Reprinted by permission of Houghton Mifflin Company. All Rights Reserved

NOTE: Every effort has been made to locate the copyright owner of material reprinted in this book. Omissions brought to our attention will be corrected in subsequent editions.

Upper Saddle River, New Jersey
Boston, Massachusetts

ISBN 0-13-203705-X

1 2 3 4 5 6 7 8 9 10 10 09 08 07 06

## Letter Home

Dear Family,

Over the coming weeks, our United States history class will be reading a chapter called The Vietnam War Era. The following information will give you some background on the content your student will be studying.

During the 1960s, the Cold War defined American foreign policy. The idea that communism was a global movement that must be contained had involved the United States in the Korean peninsula in the 1950s. That same idea would embroil the United States in a protracted war in Vietnam the following decade.

France had controlled the region in Southeast Asia known as Indochina since the 1800s. By the early 1900s, a nationalist movement led by Ho Chi Minh had begun to fight for independence from French rule. Unable to earn recognition from the United States and its allies, Ho Chi Minh found support from the Soviet Union and embraced communism. As the Cold War began, President Truman sent aid to the French in Vietnam to ensure French support in the effort to contain the Soviet Union and to strengthen anticommunist forces in Western Europe. Ultimately, France failed to rein in the communist guerrillas in Vietnam and abandoned the country in 1954.

The Geneva Accords divided Vietnam into two nations, the communist North and the anticommunist South, the latter of which was supported by the United States. The government in South Vietnam, led by Ngo Dinh Diem, grew increasingly unpopular, and Ho Chi Minh stepped up efforts to reunite Vietnam as one communist nation. Guerrilla fighters in the South, known as the Vietcong, launched a full-scale insurgency against the government. President Kennedy, determined to take a strong stance against communist forces, began sending thousands of American military "advisers" who increasingly became involved in the fighting. At the end of 1963, President Johnson inherited the mounting crisis in Vietnam when President Kennedy was assassinated. The following year, a clash between North Vietnamese and U.S. forces in the Gulf of Tonkin provoked President Johnson to order airstrikes and ask for unprecedented war-making powers from Congress. The Gulf of Tonkin Resolution authorized the President "to take all necessary measures to repel any armed attack against the forces of the United States and to prevent further aggression." The Vietnam War had begun, without Congress ever having declared war.

The Vietnam War stretched on for almost ten years. Approximately one million men were drafted to serve in Vietnam, and another million volunteered. When the war ended in 1973, more than 58,000 American soldiers had died. The war divided the nation socially, politically, and economically, and in the end, Vietnam united under a communist flag.

In the weeks ahead, your student may wish to share what he or she is learning with you. Please participate in your child's educational experience through discussion and involvement.

Sincerely,

## LA ERA DE VIETNAM
# Carta para el hogar

Estimada familia,

En las próximas semanas, nuestra clase de historia de Estados Unidos va a leer un capítulo llamado "La era de Vietnam". La siguiente información le dará a usted algunos conocimientos sobre el tema que su estudiante va a estudiar.

Durante la década de 1960, la Guerra Fría definió la política exterior de Estados Unidos. La idea de que el comunismo era un movimiento mundial que debía ser contenido involucró a Estados Unidos en la península de Corea en la década de 1950. Esa misma idea haría que Estados Unidos participara en una guerra preventiva en Vietnam la siguiente década.

Francia había controlado la región del sureste de Asia conocida como Indochina desde el siglo XIX. A comienzos del siglo XX, un movimiento nacionalista liderado por Ho Chi Minh había comenzado a luchar por la independencia del gobierno francés. Sin posibilidad de obtener reconocimiento de Estados Unidos y sus aliados, Ho Chi Minh encontró apoyo en la Unión Soviética y adoptó el comunismo. A medida que comenzaba la Guerra Fría, el presidente Truman envió ayuda a los franceses en Vietnam para que contuvieran a la Unión Soviética y para fortalecer las fuerzas anticomunistas en Europa del Este. Por fin, Francia perdió el control ante las guerrillas comunistas en Vietnam y abandonó el país en 1954.

Los acuerdos de Ginebra dividieron a Vietnam en dos naciones, el norte comunista y el sur anticomunista, que estaba apoyado por Estados Unidos. El gobierno de Vietnam del Sur, liderado por Ngo Dinh Diem, perdió popularidad y Ho Chi Minh aumentó los esfuerzos por reunificar Vietnam en una nación comunista. Los guerrilleros del sur, conocidos como Vietcong, lanzaron una insurgencia a toda escala contra el gobierno. El presidente Kennedy, determinado a tomar una posición fuerte en contra de las fuerzas comunistas, comenzó a enviar a miles de "asesores" militares estadounidenses que se vieron involucrados cada vez más en la lucha. A fines de 1963, el presidente Johnson heredó la creciente crisis en Vietnam cuando el presidente Kennedy fue asesinado. Al año siguiente, una batalla entre las fuerzas de Vietnam del Norte y las fuerzas estadounidenses en el golfo de Tonkin provocó que el presidente Johnson ordenara ataques aéreos y solicitó poderes sin precedentes para hacer la guerra al Congreso. La Resolución del golfo de Tonkin autorizó al presidente a "tomar todas mas medidas necesarias para repeler cualquier ataque armado en contra de las fuerzas de Estados Unidos y par prevenir más agresiones". Había comenzado la Guerra de Vietnam, sin que el Congreso de Estados Unidos hubiera declarado la guerra.

La Guerra de Vietnam duró casi diez años. Más de un millón de hombres fueron enrolados para ir a Vietnam, y otro millón se inscribieron como voluntarios. Cuando la guerra terminó en 1973, más de 58,000 soldados estadounidenses habían muerto. La guerra dividió al país social, política y económicamente, y al final, Vietnam se unió bajo una bandera comunista.

En las próximas semanas, es posible que su estudiante quiera compartir con usted lo que ha aprendido. Por favor participe en la experiencia educativa de su hijo o hija a través de conversaciones e involucrándose en su trabajo.

Atentamente,

**THE VIETNAM WAR ERA 1954–1975**

# 1. Origins of the Vietnam War

**Pacing**
1.5 periods
.75 block

**L1** Special Needs
**L2** Basic to Average
**L3** All Students
**L4** Average to Advanced

### Section Objectives

■ Describe the reasons that the United States helped the French fight the Vietnamese.

■ Identify the ways in which the United States opposed communism in Southeast Asia.

■ Analyze how the United States increased its involvement in Vietnam.

**Terms and People** • Ho Chi Minh • domino theory • Dien Bien Phu • SEATO • Vietcong • Gulf of Tonkin Resolution

**Focus Question:** Why did the United States become involved in Vietnam?

## PREPARE TO READ

**Build Background Knowledge**
Preview the section, and remind students that the United States wanted to contain communism.

**Set a Purpose**
Have students discuss the Witness History Selection. Point out the Section Focus Question, and have students fill in the Note Taking graphic organizer.

**Preview Key Terms**
Preview the section's Key Terms.

**Instructional Resources**
❏ **WITNESS HISTORY** Audio CD

❏ **All in One Teaching Resources**
   **L3** Preread the Chapter, p. 8
   **L3** Analyze Visuals, p. 10
   **L3** Vocabulary Builder, p. 11

❏ **Reading and Note Taking Study Guide**
   (On-Level, Adapted, and Spanish)
   Section 1

## TEACH

**America and the War in Indochina**
Explain why President Truman decided to send aid to France.

**America Opposes Communism in Vietnam**
Explore the escalation of U.S. involvement in South Vietnam.

**Johnson Leads the Nation Into War**
Clarify the reasons behind and the consequences of the Gulf of Tonkin Resolution.

**Instructional Resources**
❏ **All in One Teaching Resources**
   **L1 L2** Outline Map: Vietnam, p. 19
   **L3** Outline Map: Spread of Communism in Asia, p. 20

❏ **Color Transparencies**
   **L3** Rising U.S. Involvement in Vietnam
❏ **Note Taking Transparencies,** B-133

## ASSESS/RETEACH

**Assess Progress**
Evaluate student comprehension with the Section Assessment and Section Quiz.

**Reteach**
Assign the Reading and Note Taking Study Guide to help struggling students.

**Extend**
Have students write a paragraph about the effect of the Gulf of Tonkin Resolution on checks and balances as set forth in the Constitution.

**Instructional Resources**
❏ **All in One Teaching Resources**
   **L3** Section Quiz, p. 25
❏ **Reading and Note Taking Study Guide**
   (On-Level, Adapted, and Spanish)
   Section 1 Summary
❏ **Progress Monitoring Transparencies,** 129

**Audio support is available for this section.**
**Modify lesson with notes found on the bottom of the Teacher's Edition.**

**THE VIETNAM WAR ERA 1954–1975**

# 2. U.S. Involvement Grows

*Pacing*
2 periods
1 block

| | |
|---|---|
| **L1** | Special Needs |
| **L2** | Basic to Average |
| **L3** | All Students |
| **L4** | Average to Advanced |

## Section Objectives

- Identify the factors that caused President Johnson to increase American troop strength in Vietnam.
- Assess the nature of the war in Vietnam and the difficulties faced by both sides.
- Evaluate the effects of low morale on American troops and on the home front.

**Terms and People** • William Westmoreland • napalm • hawk • dove

**Focus Question:** What were the causes and effects of America's growing involvement in the Vietnam War?

## PREPARE TO READ

**Build Background Knowledge**
Preview the section, and point out that the Vietcong used guerrilla warfare tactics that favored small skirmishes.

**Set a Purpose**
Have students discuss the Witness History Selection. Point out the Section Focus Question, and have students fill in the Note Taking graphic organizer.

**Preview Key Terms**
Preview the section's Key Terms.

**Instructional Resources**
- ❏ **WITNESS HISTORY** Audio CD
- ❏ **Reading and Note Taking Study Guide** (On-Level, Adapted, and Spanish) Section 2

## TEACH

**"Americanizing" the War**
Explore U.S. war strategies in Vietnam and the tactics used by the Vietcong.

**Patriotism, Heroism, and Sinking Morale**
Explain the effects on American soldiers of the fighting, the environment, and the attitudes of the American and Vietnamese peoples.

**Doubt Grows on the Home Front**
Discuss the emergence of the antiwar movement.

**Instructional Resources**
- ❏ **All in One Teaching Resources**
  **L3** Reading a Chart: War Weakens the Economy, p. 21
- ❏ **Color Transparencies**
  **L3** Conflict on the Home Front
- ❏ **Note Taking Transparencies,** B-134

## ASSESS/RETEACH

**Assess Progress**
Evaluate student comprehension with the Section Assessment and Section Quiz.

**Reteach**
Assign the Reading and Note Taking Study Guide to help struggling students.

**Extend**
Ask students to write brief paragraphs explaining how Vietnam's environment contributed to the low morale of U.S. troops fighting there.

**Instructional Resources**
- ❏ **All in One Teaching Resources**
  **L3** Section Quiz, p. 26
- ❏ **Reading and Note Taking Study Guide** (On-Level, Adapted, and Spanish) Section 2 Summary
- ❏ **Progress Monitoring Transparencies,** 130

**Audio support is available for this section.**
**Modify lesson with notes found on the bottom of the Teacher's Edition.**

THE VIETNAM WAR ERA 1954–1975

# 3. The War Divides America

*Pacing*
2 periods
1 block

| L1 Special Needs |
| L2 Basic to Average |
| L3 All Students |
| L4 Average to Advanced |

## Section Objectives

■ Describe the divisions within American society over the Vietnam War.

■ Analyze the Tet Offensive and the American reaction to it.

■ Summarize the factors that influenced the outcome of the 1968 presidential election.

**Terms and People** • draftee • SDS • "credibility gap" • Tet Offensive • Eugene McCarthy • Robert Kennedy

**Focus Question:** How did the American war effort in Vietnam lead to rising protests and social divisions back home?

## PREPARE TO READ

**Build Background Knowledge**
Preview the section, and remind students that many Americans were beginning to question U.S. involvement in Vietnam.

**Set a Purpose**
Have students discuss the Witness History Selection. Point out the Section Focus Question, and have students fill in the Note Taking graphic organizer.

**Preview Key Terms**
Preview the section's Key Terms.

**Instructional Resources**
❑ **WITNESS HISTORY** Audio CD

❑ **All in One Teaching Resources**
   L3 Reading Strategy, p. 12
❑ **Reading and Note Taking Study Guide**
   (On-Level, Adapted, and Spanish)
   Section 3

## TEACH

**Antiwar Protests Increase**
Discuss the use of the draft and the rise in antiwar activism.

**Tet Offensive Is the Turning Point**
Analyze the effects of the Tet Offensive.

**Violence Rocks 1968 Presidential Race**
Summarize the events and the outcome of the 1968 presidential election.

**Instructional Resources**
❑ **All in One Teaching Resources**
   L3 Viewpoints: Can the United States Win the War in Vietnam?, p. 22
❑ **Color Transparencies**
   L3 Protesting the Vietnam War
❑ **Note Taking Transparencies,** B-135

## ASSESS/RETEACH

**Assess Progress**
Evaluate student comprehension with the Section Assessment and Section Quiz.

**Reteach**
Assign the Reading and Note Taking Study Guide to help struggling students.

**Extend**
Have students write brief persuasive paragraphs arguing for or against a draft in the United States.

**Instructional Resources**
❑ **All in One Teaching Resources**
   L3 Section Quiz, p. 27
❑ **Reading and Note Taking Study Guide**
   (On-Level, Adapted, and Spanish)
   Section 3 Summary
❑ **Progress Monitoring Transparencies,** 131

**Audio support is available for this section.**
**Modify lesson with notes found on the bottom of the Teacher's Edition.**

THE VIETNAM WAR ERA 1954–1975

# 4. The War's End and Impact

*Pacing*
2 periods
1 block

| | |
|---|---|
| **L1** | Special Needs |
| **L2** | Basic to Average |
| **L3** | All Students |
| **L4** | Average to Advanced |

## Section Objectives

- Assess Nixon's new approach to the war, and explain why protests continued.

- Explain what led to the Paris Peace Accords and why South Vietnam eventually fell to the communists.

- Evaluate the impact of the Vietnam War on the United States.

**Terms and People** • Vietnamization • Kent State University • My Lai • Pentagon Papers • Paris Peace Accords • War Powers Act

**Focus Question:** How did the Vietnam war end, and what were its lasting effects?

## PREPARE TO READ

### Build Background Knowledge
Preview the section, and point out that President Nixon inherited a nation that was deeply divided over the Vietnam War.

### Set a Purpose
Have students discuss the Witness History Selection. Point out the Section Focus Question, and have students fill in the Note Taking graphic organizer.

### Preview Key Terms
Preview the section's Key Terms.

### Instructional Resources
❑ **WITNESS HISTORY** Audio CD
❑ **Reading and Note Taking Study Guide**
(On-Level, Adapted, and Spanish)
Section 4

## TEACH

### Nixon Starts the Pullout
Explain President Nixon's policies.

### Troubles on the Home Front Intensify
Analyze the significance of the Pentagon Papers.

### The War Finally Ends
Summarize how the Vietnam War ended.

### The Vietnam War Has a Lasting Impact
Explore the impact of the Vietnam War on the United States and Southeast Asia.

### Instructional Resources
❑ **All in One Teaching Resources**
  **L3** Issues Connector: America and the World, p. 15
  **L3** Link to Literature: *The Things They Carried*, p. 23
❑ **Color Transparencies**
  **L3** The Vietnam Veterans Memorial
❑ **Note Taking Transparencies,** B-136a, B-136b

## ASSESS/RETEACH

### Assess Progress
Evaluate student comprehension with the Section Assessment and Section Quiz.

### Reteach
Assign the Reading and Note Taking Study Guide to help struggling students.

### Extend
Have students build a model of the Vietnam Veterans Memorial.

### Instructional Resources
❑ **All in One Teaching Resources**
  **L4** Enrichment: Build a Model, p. 13
  **L3** Section Quiz, p. 28
❑ **Reading and Note Taking Study Guide**
(On-Level, Adapted, and Spanish)
Section 4 Summary
❑ **Progress Monitoring Transparencies,** 132

**THE VIETNAM WAR ERA 1954–1975**

# 5. Nixon and the Cold War

*Pacing*
2 periods
1 block

L1 Special Needs
L2 Basic to Average
L3 All Students
L4 Average to Advanced

## Section Objectives

- Explain the thinking behind Richard Nixon's foreign policy.
- Define Nixon's foreign policy toward China and the Soviet Union.

**Terms and People** • Henry Kissinger • realpolitik • Zhou Enlai • Strategic Arms Limitation Treaty • détente

**Focus Question:** How did Richard Nixon change Cold War diplomacy during his presidency?

### PREPARE TO READ

**Build Background Knowledge**
Preview the section, and remind students that many foreign policy strategists believed that communism was a global movement controlled by the Soviet Union and China.

**Set a Purpose**
Have students discuss the Witness History Selection. Point out the Section Focus Question, and have students fill in the Note Taking graphic organizer.

**Preview Key Terms**
Preview the section's Key Terms.

**Instructional Resources**
❏ **WITNESS HISTORY** Audio CD
❏ **Reading and Note Taking Study Guide**
(On-Level, Adapted, and Spanish)
Section 5

### TEACH

**Nixon Redefines American Foreign Policy**
Explain the meaning of realpolitik.

**Playing the China Card**
Analyze President Nixon's efforts to open diplomatic relations with China.

**Détente With the Soviet Union**
Discuss the significance of SALT I and the easing of tensions with the Soviet Union.

**Instructional Resources**
❏ **All in One Teaching Resources**
L3 History Comics: Nixon Goes to China
❏ **Skills Handbook**
L3 Identify Evidence, p. 14
❏ **Note Taking Transparencies,** B-137

### ASSESS/RETEACH

**Assess Progress**
Evaluate student comprehension with the Section Assessment and Section Quiz.

**Reteach**
Assign the Reading and Note Taking Study Guide to help struggling students.

**Extend**
Have students research the current state of relations between China and Taiwan and between the United States and Taiwan.

**Instructional Resources**
❏ **All in One Teaching Resources**
L3 Section Quiz, p. 29
L1 L2 Chapter Test A, p. 30
L3 Chapter Test B, p. 33
❏ **Reading and Note Taking Study Guide**
(On-Level, Adapted, and Spanish)
Section 5 Summary
❏ **Progress Monitoring Transparencies,** 133

**Audio support is available for this section.**
**Modify lesson with notes found on the bottom of the Teacher's Edition.**

THE VIETNAM WAR ERA

# Preread the Chapter: Why and How?

What is **Prereading?** It is a reading comprehension strategy. This graphic organizer aids you in prereading this chapter.

**Checklist:** *Place a check on the line when you have completed the following:*

_____ Read all items in the Chapter Opener.

_____ Read the titles of the charts, graphs, maps, and timeline in the Quick Study Guide and Concept Connector Cumulative Review.

_____ Read the chapter assessment.

Before you read each section of your text, look at the following material. (Chapters may have 3, 4, or 5 sections.) Check the sections as you complete the review.

Sections: 1_____ 2_____ 3_____ 4_____ 5_____ Read the Focus Question, the section opener information in the side column, and each boldface heading and subheading.

Sections: 1_____ 2_____ 3_____ 4_____ 5_____ Looked over all words that are underlined or in boldface type.

Sections: 1_____ 2_____ 3_____ 4_____ 5_____ Read all review questions within the section.

*Complete the following:*

**1.** Chapter title: _____

**2.** Write the main idea of each section based on its Focus Question.

Section 1: _____

_____

Section 2: _____

_____

Section 3: _____

_____

Section 4: _____

_____

Section 5: _____

_____

## *Preread the Chapter: Why and How?* (Continued)

**3.** List three visual aids included in the chapter (e.g., pictures, maps, charts, diagrams, features). Describe how they will aid your understanding of the chapter.

(1) _____

_____

(2) _____

_____

(3) _____

_____

**4.** Describe one new or important idea you learned from reading the Quick Study Guide.

_____

_____

**5.** Identify two unfamiliar words that you noticed during your prereading, and determine from the context what you think the new word means.

Word #1 _____ Part of Speech _____

Clues to meaning _____

Predicted meaning _____

Word #2 _____ Part of Speech _____

Clues to meaning _____

Predicted meaning _____

**6.** After previewing this chapter, were you able to understand what the chapter is about?

Not understood _____ Somewhat understood _____ Easily understood _____

**7.** Copy the heading (titles in blue print) that you predict will be the most difficult to understand.

_____

_____

**8.** How many pages are in the chapter? _____

**9.** Estimate the time it will take you to read the chapter. _____

# Analyze Visuals

Images are an effective way to communicate information. There are many types of visuals, such as photographs, paintings, and Infographics. Visuals tell a story in a dramatic or vivid style. Just as with any primary or secondary source, it is important to look closely and ask questions to determine the meaning and reliability of the visual.

Use this outline to help you better understand ideas or events conveyed by a visual. Answer these questions to the best of your ability.

Title of visual  Page

1. What is the topic of the visual (what is happening)?

   _____

2. Focus on the details and list three that you find in the visual. How does each help convey information about the topic?

   _____

   _____

   _____

3. Assume you are one of the individuals in the picture, or that you were present when the image was made.

   (a) Describe who you are.

   _____

   (b) Explain what your reaction might have been to the situation.

   _____

   _____

4. The creator often reveals a bias about the subject or an attempt to get a response from the viewer. Is there anything you see in the image that tells the creator's point of view?

   _____

   _____

5. Write your own caption for the image.

   _____

**THE VIETNAM WAR ERA**

# Vocabulary Builder

## Make Connections

Your American history text deals with events that happened in the past. Many of the events discussed occurred long before you were even born. As you learn new vocabulary, you may find it helpful to connect words and meanings to current events in your community, the nation, and the world. Making connections in this way will help you remember and understand unfamiliar and difficult terms. The example below provides a sentence connecting the word *ensure* to modern circumstances.

> **Example**
> **Word** ensure
> **Definition** to guarantee; to secure
> **Connection to current events** The President of the United States says that he wants to <u>ensure</u> the security of all Americans.

**Directions:** *Record the definition in your textbook for each word listed below. Then, write a sentence for each word that connects it to current events. If you need help making a connection between a word and current events, skim a newspaper or news magazine for ideas.*

1. auspices _____

   **Connection to current events** _____

   _____

2. doctrine _____

   **Connection to current events** _____

   _____

3. assert _____

   **Connection to current events** _____

   _____

4. deferment _____

   **Connection to current events** _____

   _____

5. inevitable _____

   **Connection to current events** _____

   _____

6. induce _____

   **Connection to current events** _____

   _____

7. pragmatic _____

   **Connection to current events** _____

   _____

Name _____ Class _____ Date _____

# Reading Strategy

## Recognize Sequence

History is a record of human events as they have occurred over time. Learning to recognize the sequence in which events have occurred will help you examine how events connect to one another and how some events may have caused others.

Events in history texts are not always described in chronological order. To recognize sequence, you need to look for clues that tell you when things happened. Dates indicate the exact order in which events took place. Signal words, such as *then, before, after, during,* and *following* tell you when an event occurred in relation to another event. Making a list or timeline of events that includes dates and signal words will help you put events in order. Then, you can ask questions to determine whether events are related: Did two events happen at the same time? Did one event cause another?

Read the following paragraph about the draft system in the United States:

> By 1965, most of the troops sent to Vietnam were no longer volunteers who had enlisted in the army. Instead, they were draftees—young men drafted into military service—who had been assigned a tour in Vietnam. In accordance with the Selective Service Act of 1948, the government drafted more than 2 million men into military service during the Vietnam War. . . . However, critics of the Selective service system argued that the draft was not fair. . . . Speaking at a New York church in 1967, Martin Luther King, Jr., said that the war was hurting both poor blacks and whites. . . . Perceived inequities in the draft led to widespread resistance. Antiwar advocates sponsored a Stop-the-Draft week in October 1967, and some draft-eligible males burned their draft cards in protest. Finally, in 1969, the Selective Service System adopted a lottery that was designed to eliminate deferment abuses and create a more diverse army of draftees.

The circled words and phrases are dates and signal words that tell you when events happened in relation to one another: 1. The Selective Service Act was passed in 1948. 2. Congress used the act during the Vietnam War to draft more than 2 million men. 3. By 1965, draftees outnumbered volunteers. 4. Inequities in the system caused resistance. 5. King spoke against the draft in 1967. 6. Antiwar activists organized a Stop-the-Draft week in October 1967. 7. In 1969, the Selective Service System adopted a lottery.

**Directions:** *Read the section entitled "Tet Offensive Is the Turning Point" in Section 3 in your textbook. On a separate sheet of paper, list, in order, the important events about which you learned. Then, answer the questions below.*

> **Hint:** As you read, look for dates and signal words that will help you place events in sequence.

1. What was the immediate outcome of the Tet Offensive?

2. What other events resulted in part from the Tet Offensive?

3. How were the events surrounding Eugene McCarthy, Robert Kennedy, and President Johnson related?

# Enrichment: Build a Model

## The Vietnam Veterans Memorial

In 1980, President Jimmy Carter signed legislation providing a site in Washington, D.C., for the construction of the Vietnam Veterans Memorial to honor the military personnel who died or were declared missing in action during the Vietnam War. The Vietnam Veterans Memorial Fund then held a national design competition. The design submitted by a Yale University undergraduate student, Maya Lin, was selected from 1,421 entries. Lin designed the sculpture to harmonize with the surroundings of Constitutional Park. The memorial also includes a bronze sculpture, "Three Servicemen," done by Frederic Hart. In 1993, the Vietnam Women's Memorial, a sculpture of three women in uniform and a wounded soldier, designed by Glenda Goodacre, was added. Today, the Vietnam Veterans Memorial contains 58,249 names and attracts thousands of visitors every year.

**Your assignment:** Work in groups to research the design and construction of the Vietnam Veterans Memorial wall. Then, use what you learn to build a model of the memorial and a display explaining the purpose, process, and details of its construction.

**Suggested Materials:** craft supplies, such as wood, clay, plastic, foam, cardboard, paint, markers, tape, glue, and scissors; poster board to prepare your display; photographs or other images to enhance your display

**Suggested procedures:**

1. Decide what research your group needs to do and which tasks each group member will undertake.

2. Use the worksheet on the next page to help guide your research. Be sure to take the time to explore the history behind the memorial: Why did the artist design the memorial in the way that she did? What was controversial about the memorial? How have people responded to the memorial since its construction?

3. Meet together as a group and share what you have learned.

4. Collect images, such as photographs, to use on your display.

5. Work together to ensure that the model and display compliment each other.

6. Have someone volunteer to present the model and display to the class.

7. Include a summary with your display that explains the purpose of the memorial. Explain why you do or do not think the memorial is a significant part of the American cultural landscape.

Name _____ Class _____ Date _____

# Enrichment: Build a Model

## The Vietnam Veterans Memorial

*Use this worksheet to guide your research by finding the information indicated.*

1. Criteria for the design:_____
   _____
   _____

2. Purpose of the memorial:_____
   _____
   _____

3. Controversy about the memorial: _____
   _____
   _____

4. Shape and size of the memorial: _____
   _____
   _____

5. Materials used in the construction: _____
   _____
   _____

6. Maya Lin's vision or reasoning behind the design: _____
   _____
   _____

7. Criteria for and arrangement of the names on the wall: _____
   _____
   _____

8. Meaning of symbols and dates on the memorial: _____
   _____
   _____

9. Other details or statistics about the memorial: _____
   _____
   _____

10. Legacy or significance of the memorial: _____
    _____
    _____

# Issues Connector: America and the World

## George Washington's Farewell Address (1796)

When President Washington left office in 1796, he left with two fears: that Americans would become divided by political parties and that the United States would become embroiled in the conflicts of Europe. On September 19, 1796, Washington published his Farewell Address in *The American Daily Advertiser*. In it, Washington warned his fellow citizens against becoming entangled in foreign alliances with other nations. He urged them to work cooperatively with the world, and encouraged open trade for the mutual benefit of the nations involved, but he advised that forming permanent alliances based on affection or antipathy could only hurt the United States. Washington wanted the United States always to act in its own best interests.

## Monroe Doctrine (1823)

After the Napoleonic Wars in 1815, the Spanish colonies began to crumble. By 1823, Argentina, Chile, and Venezuela had declared independence. President James Monroe and his Secretary of State, John Quincy Adams, watched the developments among their neighbors with interest and caution. The European imperial powers of France, Great Britain, Russia, and Spain continued to vie for power and influence, and France and Spain came close to starting another war. The United States did not yet have the military power to confront these nations but it did not want them intruding in the Western Hemisphere. On December 2, 1823, President Monroe delivered a message to Congress that became known as the Monroe Doctrine. The Doctrine, largely engineered by Adams, stated that the American continents were closed to European colonization and that the United States would not intervene in European affairs and expected Europe to stay out of American affairs. At the time, the Monroe Doctrine received little attention from European nations, but it became a central tenet of U.S. foreign policy in the mid-1800s when President James K. Polk used its principles to keep Spain and Great Britain out of North America.

## Spanish-American War (1898)

Although the Monroe Doctrine closed the Western Hemisphere to further European colonization, it recognized the rights of European nations to existing colonies. In 1898, one of those colonies entangled the United States in conflict. Cuba declared its independence and went to war against its Spanish colonial rulers in 1895. A combination of sympathy for the Cuban revolutionaries, ire at the unexplained bombing of the USS *Maine*, and economic interests in the Cuban sugar trade prompted the U.S. Congress to declare Cuba's right to independence and demand that Spain withdraw from the island. Spain responded by declaring war against the United States, and the United States responded in kind. The Spanish-American War lasted only a few months, but it forever changed the role of the United States in the world. The Treaty of Paris, signed in 1898, ceded control of Guam, the Philippines, and Puerto Rico to the United States and put the nation in temporary control of Cuba. The United States was suddenly an imperial power as well.

# Issues Connector: America and the World

## Cold War (1950s–1990s)

Over the course of the early 1900s, the United States became increasingly involved in world affairs and emerged from World War II as one of two global superpowers. The ensuing struggles among the United States, the Soviet Union, and both countries' allies came to be known as the Cold War. An American journalist, Walter Lippmann, popularized the term *cold war* to describe the state of war without warfare that existed between the democratic, capitalist United States and the communist Soviet Union. Throughout the Cold War, these nations clashed politically, economically, and ideologically without actually declaring war or engaging in armed conflict with each other. However, the United States and the Soviet Union did engage in armed conflict through other nations such as North and South Korea and North and South Vietnam. During the Cold War, the United States established military alliances with European nations, forming the North Atlantic Treaty Organization (NATO) in 1949, and with Asian nations, forming the Southeast Asian Treaty Organization (SEATO) in 1955, and increasingly became involved in conflicts on every continent. The United States had drastically changed the course of its foreign policy since President Washington offered his Farewell Address. At the onset of the Cold War, President Harry S. Truman introduced this new foreign policy in what came to be known as the Truman Doctrine, declaring that U.S. aid should be given to any free people resisting coercion by totalitarian regimes. This policy obliged the United States to actively counter Soviet expansion by containing, or limiting, the spread of communism around the world.

## War on Terrorism (2000s)

The Cold War ended with the collapse of the Soviet Union in 1991. Suddenly, the United States was the sole superpower on a whole new playing field of world political and economic interests. Whereas the United States had for decades intervened in conflicts around the world to contain communism, the nation now had to redefine its role in the world. Throughout much of the 1990s, the United States followed a general policy of humanitarian intervention and peacekeeping in places such as Angola, Bosnia, Kosovo, and Somalia under the direction of President Bill Clinton. The United States also remained heavily involved in the Middle East, particularly in the peace negotiations between Israel and Palestine. The events of September 11, 2001, forced the United States to reexamine its goals and responsibilities. On that day, terrorists affiliated with al-Qaeda, a radical Islamic group, seized control of four planes and used them to attack the World Trade Center and the Pentagon. The attacks resulted in the deaths of approximately 3,000 people, most of them Americans. In response, President George W. Bush declared a war on terrorism that drastically altered U.S. foreign policy. For the first time, the President of the United States declared the nation's preeminence, or authority, in the world, asserted its right to preemptive war, and made the advance of global democracy the official policy of the nation.

# Issues Connector: America and the World

"The nation which indulges toward another an habitual hatred or an habitual fondness is in some degree a slave.... The great rule of conduct for us in regard to foreign nations is, in extending our commercial relations to have with them as little political connection as possible."

—*George Washington, Farewell Address, September 19, 1796*

## America and the World

"Across the generations we have proclaimed the imperative of self-government, because no one is fit to be a master, and no one deserves to be a slave.... Advancing these ideals is the mission that created our Nation.... Now it is the urgent requirement of our nation's security, and the calling of our time. So it is the policy of the United States to seek and support the growth of democratic movements and institutions in every nation and culture, with the ultimate goal of ending tyranny in our world."

—*George W. Bush, Second Inaugural Address, January 20, 2005*

We have become a great nation, forced by the fact of its greatness into relations with the other nations of the earth, and we must behave as beseems a people with such responsibilities.... No weak nation that acts manfully and justly should ever have cause to fear us, and no strong power should ever be able to single us out as a subject for insolent aggression."

—*Theodore Roosevelt, Inaugural Address, March 4, 1905*

"[T]he American continents . . . are henceforth not to be considered as subjects for future colonization by any European powers.... It is impossible that the [European nations] should extend their political system to any portion of either continent without endangering our peace and happiness; nor can anyone believe that our southern brethren, if left to themselves, would adopt it of their own accord."

—*The Monroe Doctrine, December 2, 1823*

"I believe that it must be the policy of the United States to support free peoples who are resisting attempted subjugation by armed minorities or by outside pressures.... If we falter in our leadership, we may endanger the peace of the world—and we shall surely endanger the welfare of our own nation."

—*The Truman Doctrine, March 12, 1947*

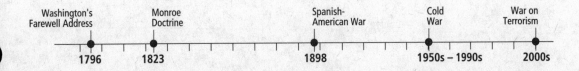

| Washington's Farewell Address | Monroe Doctrine | | | | Spanish-American War | | | Cold War | War on Terrorism |
|---|---|---|---|---|---|---|---|---|---|
| 1796 | 1823 | | | | 1898 | | | 1950s – 1990s | 2000s |

## THE VIETNAM WAR ERA

# Issues Connector

## America and the World

**Directions:** *Read the excerpts regarding the United States and its involvement in world affairs. Then, complete the chart below by writing a brief summary of each President's foreign policy, and, on a separate sheet of paper, answer the questions that follow.*

| | |
|---|---|
| George Washington | |
| James Monroe | |
| Theodore Roosevelt | |
| Harry S. Truman | |
| George W. Bush | |

1. **Synthesize Information** How has the foreign policy of the United States changed over the past two centuries?

2. **Draw Inferences** Given what you know of history, what events do you think contributed to the changes in foreign policy as expressed by these five Presidents?

3. **Compare and Contrast** To what ideals do these Presidents appeal, and what reasoning do they use to justify their policies? Point out similarities and differences among their statements.

4. **Link Past and Present** Given events in the world today, which of these policies do you think the United States should follow? Explain your answer.

**THE VIETNAM WAR ERA**

# Outline Map

## Vietnam

**Directions:** *Locate and label Vietnam, Laos, Cambodia, Thailand, the South China Sea, the Gulf of Tonkin, Saigon, Hanoi, and the Ho Chi Minh Trail. Draw a line from the Gulf of Tonkin, Saigon, Hanoi, and the Ho Chi Minh Trail to a space outside the map, where you can write a brief explanation about the importance of the place to the history of the Vietnam War. You may use any map in the textbook chapter, unit opener, or Atlas for reference.*

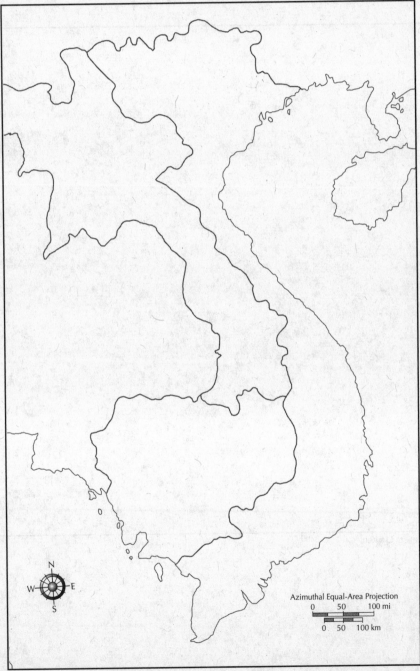

Azimuthal Equal-Area Projection
0    50    100 mi
0    50    100 km

Mapping Specialists Limited

## THE VIETNAM WAR ERA

# Outline Map

## Spread of Communism in Asia

**Directions:** *Locate and draw a line around all of the countries that once made up the Union of the Soviet Socialist Republics (USSR), or the Soviet Union. Then, locate and draw a line around any former or current communist countries in Asia. Shade in and label the nations that remain under communist rule today. On a separate sheet of paper, make a timeline showing when each nation came under communist rule. You may use any map in the textbook chapter, unit opener, or Atlas for reference.*

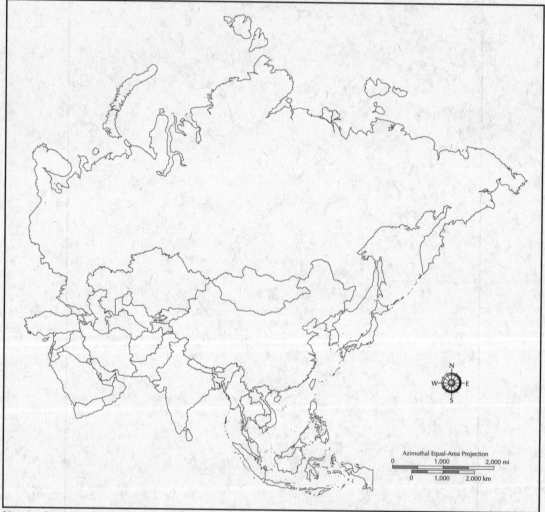

Mapping Specialists Limited

**THE VIETNAM WAR ERA**

# Reading a Chart

Estimates indicate that the total cost of the Vietnam War to the United States amounted to more than $150 billion. During the war, federal spending continually increased, driving up the public debt and raising the price of goods. The charts below illustrate the change in federal expenditures, or spending, as well as changes in the public debt and the Consumer Price Index from 1960 to 1970. The Consumer Price Index, commonly called the inflation rate, measures the average change in prices paid by consumers. Prices go up as demand for items increases and supply decreases. ♦ *Study the charts below and re-read the passage entitled "The War Weakens the Economy" in Section 2 of your textbook. Then, on a separate sheet of paper, answer the questions that follow.*

## War Weakens the Economy

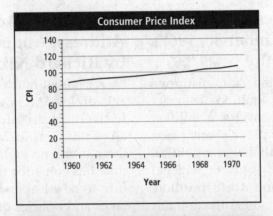

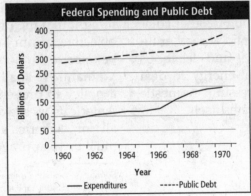

SOURCE: *Historical Statistics of the United States: Colonial Times to 1970,*
*U.S. Bureau of the Census: Washington, D.C., 1975*

## Questions to Think About

1. What do these charts indicate about federal expenditures, public debt, and inflation rates during the 1960s?

2. Which figure rose the fastest and the most?

3. **Interpret Charts** From the data above, what can you conclude about the relationship between federal expenditures and public debt?

4. **Draw Conclusions** Why do you think federal spending and the price of goods increased during the Vietnam War?

## THE VIETNAM WAR ERA

# Viewpoints

The Vietnam War caused sharp divisions among Americans, leading to a bitter presidential race in 1968 and thousands of protests involving hundreds of thousands of people all over the nation. Officials and citizens disagreed over whether the United States should continue to fight the war in Vietnam. During the 1968 presidential election, several candidates ran on an antiwar platform, including Eugene McCarthy. McCarthy campaigned for but did not win the Democratic nomination. Richard Nixon ran for and won the 1968 election on the Republican ticket. He became President in 1969. ◆ *Read the passages below, and think about why these two men might hold different opinions about U.S. involvement in Vietnam. Then, on a separate sheet of paper, answer the questions that follow.*

## Can the United States Win the War in Vietnam?

### Comments at a Press Conference, November 30, 1967, by Eugene McCarthy

I am concerned that the Administration seems to have set no limit to the price which it is willing to pay for a military victory. . . . I am not for peace at any price, but for an honorable, rational and political solution to this war; a solution which I believe will enhance our world position, encourage the respect of our Allies and our potential adversaries, which will permit us to get the necessary attention to other commitments—both at home and abroad, militarily and not militarily—and leave us with resources and moral energy to deal effectively with the pressing domestic problems of the United States itself.

### Nomination Acceptance Address, August 8, 1968, by Richard Nixon

Never has so much military and economic and diplomatic power been used so ineffectively. And if after all of this time, and all of this sacrifice, and all of this support, there is still no end in sight, then I say the time has come for the American people to turn to new leadership not tied to the mistakes and policies of the past. That is what we offer to America. And I pledge to you tonight that the first priority foreign policy objective of our next Administration will be to bring an honorable end to the war in Vietnam. We shall not stop there. We need a policy to prevent more Vietnams. All of America's peacekeeping institutions and all of America's foreign commitments must be [reappraised].

*Source*: (1) Available online at http://www.4president.org/
speeches/mccarthy1968announcement.htm.
(2) Available online at http://www.presidentialrhetoric.com/
historicspeeches/nixon/nominationacceptance1968.html.

## Questions to Think About

1. Why does McCarthy say that he is concerned by the administration's policies?

2. What does Nixon commit to doing as his first foreign policy objective?

3. **Detect Bias** Why do you think neither man says that the war is winnable or not winnable?

4. **Contrast** How do McCarthy's and Nixon's criticisms about the war differ?

**THE VIETNAM WAR ERA**

# Link to Literature

Novelist Tim O'Brien (born in 1946) graduated college in 1968 and was drafted into the United States Army. Although he had been actively protesting the Vietnam War, he went and served as an infantry foot soldier from 1969 to 1970. When he returned from the war, O'Brien worked for a time as a newspaper reporter and began writing memoirs and stories based on his experiences in Vietnam. In 1990, he used many of the stories that he had written to compose a new book, *The Things They Carried*, in which O'Brien combines fiction and memoir into a narrative presented by a fictional version of himself. O'Brien's work offers his readers a very personal look into the lives of American soldiers in Vietnam. ♦ *As you read, think about why O'Brien might choose to share the information that he does. Then, on a separate sheet of paper, answer the questions that follow.*

## The Things They Carried

The things they carried were largely determined by necessity. Among the necessities or near-necessities were P-38 can openers, pocket knives, heat tabs, wrist watches, dog tags, mosquito repellent, chewing gum, candy, cigarettes, salt tablets, packets of Kool-Aid, lighters, matches, sewing kits, Military payment Certificates, C rations, and two or three canteens of water. Together, these items weighed between fifteen and twenty pounds, depending upon a man's habits or rate of metabolism. . . . Dave Jensen, who practiced field hygiene, carried a toothbrush, dental floss, and several hotel-size bars of soap he'd stolen on R&R in Sydney, Australia. Ted Lavender, who was scared, carried tranquilizers until he was shot in the head outside the village of Than Khe in mid-April. By necessity, and because it was SOP [standard operating procedure], they all carried steel helmets that weighed

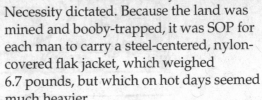

*Tim O'Brien*
**Photo credit:** Jerry Bauer

five pounds including the liner and camouflage cover. They carried the standard fatigue jackets and trousers. Very few carried underwear. On their feet they carried jungle boots—2.1 pounds— and Dave Jensen carried three pairs of socks and a can of Dr. Scholl's foot powder as a precaution against trench foot. . . . Norman Bowker carried a diary. Rat Kiley carried comic books. Kiowa, a devout Baptist, carried an illustrated New Testament that had been presented to him by his father, who taught Sunday school in Oklahoma City, Oklahoma. . . . Necessity dictated. Because the land was mined and booby-trapped, it was SOP for each man to carry a steel-centered, nylon-covered flak jacket, which weighed 6.7 pounds, but which on hot days seemed much heavier.

Source: *The Things They Carried*, by Tim O'Brien (Broadway, 1998).

## Questions to Think About

**1.** According to O'Brien, how did soldiers determine what they would carry?

**2.** Which items did soldiers carry because it was standard operating procedure? How much did these items weigh?

**3. Draw Conclusions** Dave Jensen carried extra socks and foot powder "as a precaution against trench foot." What do you think trench foot is?

**4. Draw Inferences** What do the items listed tell you about the lives of American soldiers in Vietnam? How does this passage help you relate to the soldiers?

# History Comics

In 1969, at the Yugoslavian Embassy in Poland, American officials chased after a delegation of Chinese officials. "I saw President Nixon in Washington," the U.S. ambassador told them. "He wants to establish relations with China." At the time, the United States had refused to recognize the communist government of the People's Republic of China, but President Nixon saw an opportunity to change the balance of power in the world. ◆ *Refer to the passage entitled "Nixon Normalizes Relations with China" in Section 5 of your textbook to write captions for the following comic panels.*

## Nixon Goes to China

_____

_____

Chris Vallo

_____   _____   _____
_____   _____   _____

Name _____ Class _____ Date _____

THE VIETNAM WAR ERA

# Section 1 Quiz

## A.  Key Terms and People

**Directions:** *Use the terms and people in the word bank to complete the statements below.*

| | | |
|---|---|---|
| Ho Chi Minh | domino theory | Dien Bien Phu |
| SEATO | Vietcong | Gulf of Tonkin Resolution |

1. _____ worked to contain the spread of communism in Southeast Asia.

2. President Johnson gained extraordinary war powers under the _____.

3. The Vietminh laid siege to _____, trapping a large French garrison.

4. National Liberation Front guerrilla fighters, called _____, launched an insurgency against the Diem government of South Vietnam.

5. _____ demanded independence from France and embraced communism.

6. The _____ was the idea that if Vietnam fell to communism, its closest neighbors would follow.

## B.  Key Concepts

**Directions:** *Write the letter of the best answer or ending in the space provided.*

_____ 7. President Truman agreed to help France because he
   a. supported colonialism.  c. feared the spread of communism.
   b. backed Ho Chi Minh.  d. wanted to weaken anticommunist forces.

_____ 8. The Geneva Accords provided for
   a. immediate elections in Vietnam.
   b. the division of Vietnam into two countries.
   c. French control of Cambodia, Laos, and Vietnam.
   d. an anticommunist government in control of a unified Vietnam.

_____ 9. What happened during the Vietnamese election in 1956?
   a. Ho Chi Minh cancelled the election.
   b. Ngo Dinh Diem refused to participate.
   c. Ngo Dinh Diem won an overwhelming popular victory.
   d. The United States installed Ngo Dinh Diem as president.

_____ 10. President Johnson escalated American involvement in Vietnam by
   a. declaring war.  c. sending "advisers."
   b. having Ngo Dinh Diem assassinated.  d. ordering airstrikes.

# Section 2 Quiz

## A. Key Terms and People

**Directions:** *Read the following statements. If a statement is correct, write "T" next to the sentence. If a statement is incorrect, write "F" next to the sentence and replace the underlined word(s) to make the statement correct.*

_____ 1. Agent Orange is a jellied gasoline that American pilots dropped on Vietnam.

_____ 2. Hawks disagreed with President Johnson's war policy.

_____ 3. The commander in South Vietnam was Robert McNamara.

_____ 4. The mostly conservative doves supported President Johnson's war policy.

## B. Key Concepts

**Directions:** *Write the letter of the best answer or ending in the space provided.*

_____ 5. To convince North Vietnam to stop reinforcing the Vietcong, President Johnson ordered Operation Rolling Thunder, which

    **a.** began a sustained bombing campaign.

    **b.** put more American troops on the ground.

    **c.** involved search-and-destroy missions to hunt down guerrillas.

    **d.** increased the number of American advisers in South Vietnam.

_____ 6. American soldiers used Agent Orange to

    **a.** detect Vietcong booby traps.

    **b.** disrupt the enemy's food supply.

    **c.** find each other in the jungle.

    **d.** treat wounds.

_____ 7. Ho Chi Minh compared his military to a(n)

    **a.** wasp.    **c.** snake.

    **b.** tiger.    **d.** elephant.

_____ 8. Which of the following best describes the Vietcong's war strategy?

    **a.** fight small skirmishes    **c.** engage in large-scale battles

    **b.** avoid any confrontation    **d.** battle by day and rest at night

_____ 9. By the end of 1965, most American soldiers in Vietnam

    **a.** refused to fight.    **c.** had been drafted.

    **b.** were volunteers.    **d.** had not seen any fighting.

_____ 10. Why did President Johnson have to cut back his Great Society initiatives?

    **a.** Inflation dropped.    **c.** Unemployment went up.

    **b.** Congress lowered taxes.    **d.** The cost of the war was rising.

THE VIETNAM WAR ERA

# Section 3 Quiz

## A. Key Terms and People

**Directions:** *Match each term or person in Column II below with the correct definition in Column I.*

**Column I**

_____ 1. a group formed to campaign against poverty and racism that spoke out against the war

_____ 2. an antiwar senator from Minnesota who ran for president

_____ 3. the difference between what the administration said and what journalists reported

_____ 4. a communist assault on provincial capitals, major cities, and a U.S. embassy

_____ 5. a soldier who did not volunteer to serve

_____ 6. a Democratic senator from New York who ran for the presidency

**Column II**

a. draftee

b. SDS

c. "credibility gap"

d. Tet Offensive

e. Eugene McCarthy

f. Robert Kennedy

## B. Key Concepts

**Directions:** *Write the letter of the best answer or ending in the space provided.*

_____ 7. During the Vietnam War, African American soldiers were

    a. not allowed to fight overseas.

    b. often granted deferments to attend college.

    c. becoming commissioned officers at a high rate.

    d. more likely than others to serve in combat positions.

_____ 8. To eliminate deferment abuses, the Selective Service system

    a. adopted a lottery.

    b. allowed some men to burn their draft cards.

    c. put local draft boards in charge of selection.

    d. recruited more heavily among working class and poor people.

_____ 9. In March 1968, what surprising announcement did President Johnson make to the American people?

    a. The draft had ended.

    b. He would not run for another term as President.

    c. The Vietcong had seized control of South Vietnam.

    d. The United States and South Vietnam had won the war.

_____ 10. Who won the 1968 Presidential election?

    a. Hubert Humphrey      c. Richard Nixon

    b. Robert Kennedy      d. George Wallace

# Section 4 Quiz

## A. Key Terms and People

**Directions:** *Use the terms and people in the word bank to complete the statements below.*

| | | |
|---|---|---|
| Vietnamization | Kent State University | My Lai |
| Pentagon Papers | Paris Peace Accords | War Powers Act |

1. In 1971, the _____ were leaked to *The New York Times.*

2. President Nixon hoped to withdraw U.S. forces through _____.

3. The _____ called for a cease-fire and U.S. troop withdrawal.

4. In 1973, Congress passed the _____ to stop the growth of the "imperial presidency."

5. Four people were killed during protests at _____.

6. The massacre at _____ resulted in the deaths of hundreds of Vietnamese.

## B. Key Concepts

**Directions:** *Write the letter of the best answer or ending in the space provided.*

_____ 7. President Nixon ordered the secret bombing of the Ho Chi Minh Trail in Cambodia to
   a. boost morale.          c. protect Vietnamese civilians.
   b. stop the peace process.   d. reduce the flow of communist supplies.

_____ 8. In 1970, President Nixon tried to break the stalemate in the peace process by
   a. pulling U.S. forces out of Cambodia.
   b. helping the Khmer Rouge seize power in Cambodia.
   c. ordering a ground attack on Vietcong bases in Cambodia.
   d. sending economic aid to the Cambodian government.

_____ 9. What did the Pentagon Papers reveal?
   a. President Nixon withdrew from the peace process.
   b. The United States had given arms and money to the Vietcong.
   c. The U.S. military tried to cover up the massacre of Vietnamese civilians.
   d. U.S. leaders misled Congress and the American people about the war.

_____ 10. Ultimately, the end of the Vietnam War resulted in
   a. greater U.S. involvement in Southeast Asia.
   b. expanded war-making powers for the U.S. President.
   c. communist control of Cambodia, Laos, and Vietnam.
   d. a communist North Vietnam and a democratic South Vietnam.

**THE VIETNAM WAR ERA**

# Section 5 Quiz

## A. Key Terms and People

**Directions:** *Read the following statements. If a statement is correct, write "T" next to the sentence. If a statement is incorrect, write "F" next to the sentence and replace the underlined word(s) to make the statement correct.*

_____ 1. Nixon's leading national security advisor was <u>Henry Kissinger</u>.

_____ 2. <u>Realpolitik</u> was a policy aimed at easing Cold War tensions.

_____ 3. The <u>Strategic Arms Limitation Treaty</u> froze the deployment of certain missiles.

_____ 4. Premier <u>Zhou Enlai</u> worked to have President Nixon visit China.

_____ 5. Nixon promoted <u>détente</u>, the idea that concrete national interests should define political goals.

## B. Key Concepts

**Directions:** *Write the letter of the best answer or ending in the space provided.*

_____ 6. President Nixon considered his approach to foreign policy to be

    **a.** liberal.               **c.** pragmatic.

    **b.** orthodox.            **d.** ideological.

_____ 7. President Nixon believed that normalizing relations with China would

    **a.** prolong the war in Vietnam.

    **b.** hurt American economic interests.

    **c.** damage efforts to democratize China.

    **d.** drive a wedge between China and the Soviet Union.

_____ 8. China demonstrated its willingness to open talks with the United States by

    **a.** rejecting communism.        **c.** hosting a table tennis match.

    **b.** opening trade.             **d.** limiting arms deployment.

_____ 9. How did the Soviet Union respond to the normalization of relations between China and the United States?

    **a.** Brezhnev invited Nixon to visit Moscow.

    **b.** Soviet companies set up a thriving trade with China.

    **c.** The Soviet Union cut off diplomatic relations with China.

    **d.** The Soviet space program ended its collaboration with U.S. scientists.

_____ 10. SALT I

    **a.** encouraged China to enter the arms race.

    **b.** reduced tensions between the United States and the Soviet Union.

    **c.** ended the arms race between the United States and the Soviet Union.

    **d.** sparked a renewed effort to stockpile missiles.

## THE VIETNAM WAR ERA

# Test A

## A. Key Terms and People

**Directions:** *Match the definitions in Column I with the letter of the correct term or person in Column II. (3 points each)*

**Column I**

_____ 1. a political adviser to President Nixon

_____ 2. guerrilla fighters in Vietnam

_____ 3. an attack by communist forces on more than 40 cities in Vietnam

_____ 4. rebel leader who demanded independence for Vietnam

_____ 5. an antiwar candidate for President in 1968

_____ 6. Chinese premier who held talks with President Nixon

_____ 7. a classified study of American involvement in Vietnam

_____ 8. a Vietnamese village attacked by American troops

_____ 9. a jellied gasoline that explodes when dropped in large canisters

_____ 10. the idea that if Vietnam fell to communism, its neighbors would follow

**Column II**

a. Ho Chi Minh

b. domino theory

c. Vietcong

d. napalm

e. Tet Offensive

f. Eugene McCarthy

g. My Lai

h. Pentagon Papers

i. Henry Kissinger

j. Zhou Enlai

## B. Key Concepts

**Directions:** *Write the letter of the best answer or ending in the space provided. (4 points each)*

_____ 11. According to the Geneva Accords,

    a. France would gain control of Vietnam.

    b. Vietnam would be divided into two countries.

    c. the United States would install a temporary government in Vietnam.

_____ 12. To repel attacks against U.S. troops in Vietnam, Congress passed the

    a. Geneva Accords.

    b. USS *Maddox* Resolution.

    c. Gulf of Tonkin Resolution.

_____ 13. Operation Rolling Thunder was ordered to

    a. regain control of the U.S. embassy in Saigon.

    b. prevent the North Vietnamese army from attacking the USS *Maddox*.

    c. stop North Vietnam from reinforcing Vietcong troops in South Vietnam.

Name _____ Class _____ Date _____

**Directions:** *Use the image below to answer question 14.*

**Photo Credit:** ©Bettman/CORBIS

_____ 14. This image shows the
   a. attack on My Lai.
   b. dropping of napalm.
   c. spraying of Agent Orange.

_____ 15. Antiwar protesters were called
   a. doves.
   b. hawks.
   c. guerrillas.

_____ 16. The difference between what President Johnson said and what many journalists reported was called the
   a. fact gap.
   b. media gap.
   c. credibility gap.

_____ 17. Which of the following signaled that the Vietnam War would not end quickly?
   a. Tet Offensive
   b. War Powers Act
   c. Gulf of Tonkin Resolution

_____ 18. President Nixon's "peace with honor" policy focused on
   a. ending the war without abandoning South Vietnam.
   b. continuing the war into Cambodia with more bombings.
   c. gaining more control of North Vietnam and ending the war.

_____ 19. Henry Kissinger arranged for President Nixon to visit
   a. China.
   b. France.
   c. Cambodia.

_____ 20. The Soviet Union and the United States signed which of the following to ease Cold War tensions?
   a. Geneva Accords
   b. Missile Reduction Treaty
   c. Strategic Arms Limitation Treaty

## C.  Document-Based Assessment

**Directions:** *Read the excerpt below from President Nixon's speech. Then, on the back of this paper or on a separate sheet of paper, answer question 21. (10 points)*

> "And so tonight—to you, the great silent majority of my fellow Americans—I ask for your support. I pledged in my campaign for the Presidency to end the war in a way that we could win the peace. The more support I can have from the American people, the sooner that pledge can be [fulfilled]; for the more divided we are at home, the less likely the enemy is to negotiate [reach a deal with us] at Paris. Let us be united for peace. Let us also be united against defeat. Because let us understand: North Vietnam cannot defeat or humiliate the United States. Only Americans can do that."
>
> —*President Richard Nixon, November 3, 1969*

**21. Draw Inferences** Why does Nixon say that Americans must be united?

## D.  Critical Thinking

**Directions:** *Answer the questions below on the back of this paper or on a separate sheet of paper. (10 points each)*

**22. Synthesize Information** Identify two reasons that people opposed the Vietnam War.

**23. Apply Information** Define realpolitik and explain how President Nixon's ideas about realpolitik affected his foreign policy toward China?

**THE VIETNAM WAR ERA**

# Test B

## A. Key Terms and People

**Directions:** *Match the definitions in Column I with the letter of the correct term or person in Column II. (3 points each)*

**Column I**

_____ 1. President Nixon's leading adviser on national security and international affairs

_____ 2. guerrilla fighters who launched an insurgency in Vietnam

_____ 3. a coordinated assault by communist forces on more than 40 cities in Vietnam

_____ 4. rebel leader who demanded independence for Vietnam

_____ 5. an antiwar candidate for President in 1968

_____ 6. Chinese premier who normalized relations with President Nixon

_____ 7. a classified government history of American involvement in Vietnam

_____ 8. a Vietnamese village attacked by American troops

_____ 9. a jellied gasoline that explodes when dropped in large canisters

_____ 10. the idea that if Vietnam fell to communism, its neighbors would follow

**Column II**

a. Ho Chi Minh

b. domino theory

c. Dien Bien Phu

d. Vietcong

e. Gulf of Tonkin Resolution

f. William Westmoreland

g. napalm

h. Tet Offensive

i. Eugene McCarthy

j. My Lai

k. Pentagon Papers

l. Henry Kissinger

m. Zhou Enlai

## B. Key Concepts

**Directions:** *Write the letter of the best answer or ending in the space provided. (4 points each)*

_____ 11. President Johnson entered the Vietnam War because he

    a. believed in the domino theory.

    b. ran for office as a war dove.

    c. underestimated the communist threat.

    d. wanted to institute a realpolitik policy.

_____ 12. The Gulf of Tonkin Resolution allowed President Johnson to

    a. send economic aid to South Vietnam.

    b. declare war against North Vietnam without asking Congress.

    c. use the USS *Maddox* to control the seas around South Vietnam.

    d. take all necessary measures to defend against armed attacks on U.S. forces.

_____ **13.** Operation Rolling Thunder was a(n)

    **a.** sustained bombing campaign against North Vietnam.

    **b.** strategy to regain control of the U.S. embassy in Saigon.

    **c.** plan to give South Vietnam greater military responsibility.

    **d.** offensive designed to show that North Vietnam could still fight.

**Directions:** *Use the image below to answer question 14.*

**Photo Credit:** ©Bettman/CORBIS

_____ **14.** This image shows the

    **a.** Tet Offensive.     **c.** dropping of napalm.

    **b.** attack on My Lai.     **d.** spraying of Agent Orange.

_____ **15.** Which of the following would probably be considered a hawk?

    **a.** Robert Kennedy     **c.** Eugene McCarthy

    **b.** Martin Luther King, Jr.     **d.** Richard Nixon

_____ **16.** The American public began to distrust the Johnson administration because of the

    **a.** credibility gap.     **c.** Pentagon Papers.

    **b.** War Powers Act.     **d.** 1968 Democratic Convention.

_____ **17.** Why was the Tet Offensive considered a turning point in the war?

    **a.** The United States and South Vietnam won a strategic victory.

    **b.** The massacre of unarmed civilians damaged support for the war.

    **c.** U.S. forces destroyed supply lines between North and South Vietnam.

    **d.** The Vietcong and North Vietnamese showed that they could still fight.

_____ **18.** President Nixon's Vietnamization policy emphasized that the United States must

    **a.** use any means necessary to end the war.

    **b.** open trade relations with a unified Vietnam.

    **c.** defeat communism in Vietnam to preserve other countries.

    **d.** empower South Vietnamese forces to assume more combat duties.

_____ **19.** Which country did President Nixon visit to improve trade relations?

    **a.** Cambodia                    **c.** the Soviet Union

    **b.** China                         **d.** Vietnam

_____ **20.** The Strategic Arms Limitation Treaty

    **a.** signaled the end of the conflict in Cambodia.

    **b.** eased tensions between South and North Vietnam.

    **c.** stepped up the deployment of ballistic and antiballistic missiles.

    **d.** slowed the arms race between the Soviet Union and the United States.

## C. Document-Based Assessment

**Directions:** *Read the excerpt below from President Nixon's speech. Then, on the back of this paper or on a separate sheet of paper, answer question 21. (10 points)*

> "Let historians not record that when America was the most powerful nation in the world we passed on the other side of the road and allowed the last hopes for peace and freedom of millions of people to be suffocated by the forces of totalitarianism. And so tonight—to you, the great silent majority of my fellow Americans—I ask for your support. I pledged in my campaign for the Presidency to end the war in a way that we could win the peace. I have initiated a plan of action which will enable me to keep that pledge. The more support I can have from the American people, the sooner that pledge can be redeemed; for the more divided we are at home, the less likely the enemy is to negotiate at Paris. Let us be united for peace. Let us also be united against defeat. Because let us understand: North Vietnam cannot defeat or humiliate the United States. Only Americans can do that."
>
> —*President Richard Nixon, November 3, 1969*

**21. Apply Information** How does Nixon's speech reflect his policy of "peace with honor"?

## D. Critical Thinking

**Directions:** *Answer the questions below on the back of this paper or on a separate sheet of paper. (10 points each)*

**22. Explain Problems** Why did opposition to the Vietnam War increase over time? Explain why you think the criticism of the war was or was not justified.

**23. Synthesize Information** How did President Nixon's overtures to China reflect his commitment to realpolitik?

# Answer Key

## Vocabulary Builder

Students' answers should demonstrate understanding of the vocabulary.

## Reading Strategy

1. American and South Vietnamese forces repelled the offensive.
2. Secretary of Defense Clifford advised President Johnson to pursue peace negotiations. More Americans engaged in antiwar protests. Johnson's approval dropped in the polls. Two Democratic senators challenged Johnson for the party's nomination. Johnson decided to pursue peace talks. Johnson decided not to run for another term.
3. McCarthy and Kennedy both decided to seek the Democratic Party's presidential nomination because they sensed that Johnson had little support and they wanted to change the nation's policies toward Vietnam. President Johnson decided not to run for reelection because he also sensed that he had lost support.

## Enrichment

Students' projects should demonstrate research, creative thinking, and appropriate presentation. Use Assessment Rubrics to evaluate the project.

## Issues Connector
## America and the World

1. Students may mention the nation's increasing interdependence with other nations via trade and alliances. Students may contrast the nation's military involvement around the globe with Washington's warnings against excessive entanglements.
2. Possible responses: Monroe was likely responding to continuing European expansion, the War of 1812, and the nation's reliance on foreign trade. Roosevelt became president following the Spanish-American War when the United States suddenly had control over foreign lands. Truman was responding to the events and devastation of World War II and to the emergence of two global superpowers. Bush reshaped his foreign policy in response to the September 11 attacks, as well as to the end of the Cold War.
3. Possible responses: The presidents appeal to liberal ideals of freedom and democracy as well as to the need for national security. Washington focuses on the need to protect the nation's interests. Monroe also emphasizes national security. Roosevelt points to the nation's importance in world affairs. Truman also states the United States must exercise leadership in the world. Bush says that the nation must advance liberal democratic ideals across the globe to end tyranny and protect the United States.
4. Students' responses will vary but should reflect the policy chosen.

## Outline Map
## Vietnam

Students should label the appropriate nations and provide brief explanations of their significance to the Vietnam War.

## Spread of Communism in Asia

Students should draw a line around Armenia, Azerbaijan, Belarus, Georgia, Kazakhstan, Kyrgystan, Moldova, Russia, Tajikistan, Turkmenistan, Ukraine, and Uzbekistan. Students should also draw a line around Afghanistan, Cambodia, China, Iran, Laos, Mongolia, North Korea, Vietnam, and Yemen. Students should shade and label China, Laos, North Korea, and Vietnam. Timeline should show North Korea, 1948; China, 1949; Laos, 1975; and Vietnam, 1976.

# Answer Key

## Reading a Chart
### War Weakens the Economy

1. They all went up.
2. federal expenditures
3. As the federal government spent more, it had to borrow more, so the public debt increased at almost the same rate.
4. Possible response: Federal spending increased because the government had to spend more money to supply the war effort. The price of goods went up in response to the higher demand for supplies and other goods

## Viewpoints
### Can the United States Win the War in Vietnam?

1. He is concerned that the administration will pay any price to win in Vietnam.
2. bringing an honorable end to the war
3. Nixon criticizes the conduct of the war on the part of the present administration, implying that the United States could have won the war with better leadership. McCarthy criticizes the administration's willingness to escalate the war at any cost in order to achieve a decisive victory rather than focusing on achieving peace.

## Link to Literature
### *The Things They Carried*

1. by necessity
2. steel helmets and steel-centered, nylon-covered flak jackets; 11.7 pounds
3. Possible response: The soldiers had a difficult time. They carried many things to keep them safe, to treat or prevent sickness and injury, and to use in combat. They carried extra things that they did not really need because they enjoyed them. These things may have made their lives feel more normal. The things they carried show that soldiers faced many dangers. This description helps me relate to the soldiers by showing me that they liked some of the same things that I do. It helps me understand that they were real people with everyday likes and needs.

## History Comics
### Nixon Goes to China

Richard Nixon and Mao Zedong dreamily consider normalizing relations with each other. / Nixon makes plans to visit China as Mao drafts an invite to the American President. The two nations have already made a symbolic overture to one another by agreeing to a table tennis match. / In 1972, Nixon journeys to China, where he tours the Great Wall with his wife and meets with Mao and Zhou Enlai. / The talks go well and pave the way for tourism and trade between the two nations. / Worried by the new relationship between China and the United States, Leonid Brezhnev of the Soviet Union decides to invite Nixon to Moscow.

## Section 1 Quiz

1. SEATO
2. Gulf of Tonkin Resolution
3. Dien Bien Phu
4. Vietcong
5. Ho Chi Minh
6. domino theory
7. a
8. b
9. b
10. d

## Section 2 Quiz

1. F, Napalm
2. F, Doves
3. F, William Westmoreland
4. F, hawks
5. a
6. b
7. b
8. a
9. c
10. d

## Section 3 Quiz

1. b  2. e  3. c  4. d  5. a
6. f  7. a  8. b  9. b  10. c

# Answer Key

## Section 4 Quiz

1. Pentagon Papers
2. Vietnamization
3. Paris Peace Accords
4. War Powers Act
5. Kent State University

6. My Lai
7. c
8. d
9. d
10. c

## Section 5 Quiz

1. T
2. F, Détente
3. T
4. T
5. F, realpolitik

6. c
7. d
8. c
9. a
10. b

## Test A

1. i
2. c
3. e
4. a
5. f
6. j
7. h
8. g
9. d
10. b
11. b
12. c
13. c
14. c
15. a
16. c
17. a
18. a
19. a
20. c

21. Nixon says that Americans must be united to make the enemy compromise and negotiate peace and to win peace without defeat or disgrace.

22. Possible responses: Each year, the war claimed more lives and cost more money, leading to higher taxes and reduced spending on domestic concerns. Increased spending led to inflation and rising prices. American troops did not win any large-scale battles. The draft forced men into service who did not want to fight or who did not believe in the war. The Selective Service System drafted a disproportionate number of African Americans as well as working-class and poor whites. Some Americans did not support the principle of warfare. The My Lai massacre and the Pentagon Papers caused people to believe that the government had lied to and betrayed them.

23. Realpolitik meant that officials should put practical national interests and clear foreign policy goals above abstract ideas about communism. Nixon's realpolitik thinking helped him see that China and the Soviet Union were not united and could be worked against each other. This realization led Nixon to open relations with China.

## Test B

1. l
2. d
3. h
4. a
5. i
6. m
7. k
8. j
9. g
10. b
11. a
12. d
13. a
14. d
15. d
16. a
17. d
18. d
19. b
20. d

21. President Nixon says that he has a plan to win the peace without suffering defeat or humiliation. He considers dishonorable any effort to gain peace at the expense of victory or at the expense of the power of the United States.

22. Opposition to the war increased over time because as the war continued, it claimed more lives and cost more money. These conditions led to higher taxes, reduced spending on domestic concerns, inflation, and rising prices. Over time, more men were drafted into the army who did not want to go. Many people disliked abuses in the draft system. As the violence overseas escalated and disparities between government statements and media reports increased, more people began to distrust the government's policies. The My Lai massacre and Pentagon Papers caused many people to feel betrayed. Students should explain whether they believe that these criticisms were justified.

23. Realpolitik refers to a policy in which practical national interests, rather than abstract ideologies, define clear foreign policy goals. Nixon approached China because his realpolitik thinking led him to understand that China and the Soviet Union did not form a united communist block and that they could be worked against each other to the economic and political advantage of the United States.